WHAT'S WRONG AROUND THE

Hi, we're Leah and Eddie! Join us as we travel the world and discover all sorts of interesting places and people.

But watch out! In each scene there are **five** out of place things to spot.

Can you find them all? Look carefully, as some are hard to spot. Turn to the back of the book for handy explanations about what's wrong, as well as a **strange but true!** fact per scene – these might seem wrong, but they're actually right!

LET THE SEARCH BEGIN!

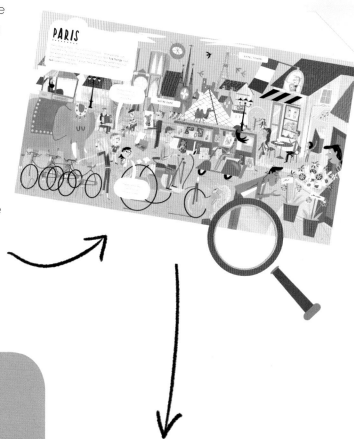

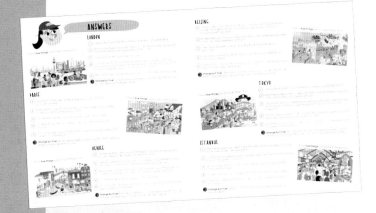

CONTENTS

LONDON

Welcome to London, the capital city of the United Kingdom.
Jump aboard and travel down the River Thames. Can you spot
five things that are wrong or don't belong here? Can you say
what's wrong with them or on which page they do belong?
There are **two** clues to help you.

LONDON EYE

HOUSES OF PARLIAMENT

PARIS

Next stop is Paris, the capital of France. Some people call Paris the city of love – ooh la la! Can you spot **five things** that are wrong or don't belong here? Can you say what's wrong with them or on which page they do belong? There are **two** clues to help you.

NOTRE-DAME

That portrait isn't of the person it should be!

There are a few out of place animals here!

VENICE

This is Venice, in Italy. Venice is a pretty, watery city, with lots of small islands, canals and bridges. Can you spot **five things** that are wrong or don't belong here? Can you say what's wrong with them or on which page they do belong? There are **two** clues to help you.

GONDOLA

RIALTO BRIDGE

CANAL

One of those homes belongs on a camping trip.

One of these animals belongs in Australia, not Venice!

BEIJING

The Great Wall of China passes through China's capital city of Beijing. It's a huuuuuuge wall built thousands of years ago across China. You need lots of puff to travel from one end to the other as it would take months to walk. Can you spot **five things** that are wrong or don't belong here? There are **two** clues to help you.

One of those trees has unusual blossom...

One of the watchtowers will blow down in a strong wind!

WATCHTOWER

10

GREAT WALL OF CHINA

11

TOKYO

Tokyo is the capital city of Japan. The emperor of Japan rules his country like a king or queen. This amazing palace is his home. Let's pop in for a cup of tea! Can you spot **five things** that are wrong or don't belong here? Can you say what's wrong with them or where they do belong? There are **two** clues to help you.

TEA HOUSE

One person drinking tea lived a long time ago.

That icy home belongs in a much colder place.

12

MOUNT FUJI

IMPERIAL PALACE

ISTANBUL

Next stop is Istanbul, Turkey. Let's explore the Grand Bazaar, meaning 'Covered Market'. There are thousands of shops and stalls here, so it will be easy to find a souvenir. Can you spot **five things** that are wrong or don't belong here? There are **two** clues to help you.

TURKISH DELIGHT

GIZA

These pyramids in Giza, Egypt were built by the Egyptians thousands of years ago. They buried their dead rulers in them. The rulers were buried with all their things, and even with their servants and pets who were still alive! Can you spot **five things** that are wrong or don't belong here? Can you say what's wrong with them or where they do belong? There are **two** clues to help you.

A sphinx statue has the body of a lion and the head of a king. One statue is not right.

One of those wheelbarrows is full of some very strange-coloured sand!

PYRAMID

SPHINX

NEW YORK

Next stop New York, in the United States of America. New York is huge, busy, noisy and packed with super-tall skyscrapers. Can you spot **five things** that are wrong or don't belong here? Can you say what's wrong with them or where they do belong? There are **two** clues to help you.

EMPIRE STATE BUILDING

People don't ride bicycles like that anymore.

There's something odd about that statue!

TAXI

TOYS

FLATIRON BUILDING

I ♥ NY

PIZZA

GALLERY

SUBWAY

RIO DE JANEIRO

Ola! That means hello in Brazil. Put on your carnival costume and join the fun in Rio de Janeiro. Can you spot **five things** that are wrong or don't belong here? Can you say what's wrong with them or where they do belong? There are **two** clues to help you.

COPACABANA

CORCOVADO MOUNTAIN

21

ANSWERS

LONDON

1. Dolphins don't live in the River Thames as it's too cold and shallow.

2. Big Ben doesn't wear a bow tie! People call this clock Big Ben, but Big Ben is really the name of the huge bell inside the clock.

3. The Eiffel Tower belongs in Paris, France.

4. London buses are red, but they only have one or two decks, not five. You would get a good view from the top deck on this bus, but it wouldn't fit under any bridges so you couldn't go far in London.

5. The Romans lived over two thousand years ago and aren't around today.

★ **Strange but true!** Lions don't walk the streets of London, but this is one of four lion statues in Trafalgar Square.

These **five things** are wrong in the picture:

PARIS

1. People don't drive cars like this today. This is one of the first cars ever invented.

2. There are lots of animals in The Paris Zoological Park, but this cheeky monkey shouldn't be hanging out here!

3. This elephant shouldn't be roaming the streets of Paris either!

4. Oh dear, this painter is not very good! He's drawn this person as a koala!

5. This camel might look at home next to a pyramid-shaped building, but camels live in the desert.

★ **Strange but true!** This building might look like a pyramid, but it's actually an art museum called the Louvre.

These **five things** are wrong in the picture:

VENICE

1. That hippopotamus doesn't live here! Hippos chomp on huge amounts of grass but they wouldn't find much of that in Venice.

2. There are no banana boats in Venice... but there are gondola boats that take tourists around the city. The drivers may even sing to you!

3. The stripy mooring pole belongs in Venice, but it shouldn't have a koala attached to it! Koalas live in the forests and woodlands of Australia.

4. Of course chickens can't paraglide, so this is wrong!

5. This tent is out of place on the streets of Venice. You might get a bit wet if you pitched your tent here!

★ **Strange but true!** Don't be spooked, this is a real person! People dress up and wear amazing masks for the annual Carnival of Venice.

These **five things** are wrong in the picture: